FIRE
WORDS

I LOVE
John
TRINE
By Janice
and A's girl
Kiss Kiss
Kiss Kiss

FIRE WORDS

COMPILED BY CHRIS SEARLE

JONATHAN CAPE
THIRTY BEDFORD SQUARE LONDON

by Chris Searle

POILU (*novel, Workshop Press*)
THE FORSAKEN LOVER (*non-fiction*)

compiled by Chris Searle and Ron McCormick
STEPNEY WORDS (*a collection of children's poetry*)

First published 1972
The copyright rests with the writer of each poem
The collection © 1972 by Jonathan Cape Ltd

Jonathan Cape Ltd, 30 Bedford Square, London WC1

ISBN Hardback 0 224 00764
ISBN Paperback 0 224 00776 9

Printed and bound in Great Britain
by Richard Clay (The Chaucer Press) Ltd
Bungay, Suffolk

I have my own identity.
I have my own ideas
With what should be done with this world.

TONY HUSSEY, 13
Spitalfields, London

Words
Are deadly,
Deadlier than any weapon,
More painful than any wound,
For words
Are messengers
Of our thoughts
And our dreads,
And words can be the spark that lands upon the dry grass
And starts the fire.

Words come tumbling out your mouth,
Hate's own tongue is all spit out,
Spread the caustic voice of yours,
Over to my ears.

Words
Are kind,
Kinder than any movement
Or any gift or thought,
For words
Are messengers
Of our thoughts
And our deeds,
And kind words can be the spark that lands on the dry grass
And starts a fire.

KEVIN HEWICK, 14
Leicester

Bonfire

A bright slim figure leaps up the fireplace,
And slips down again,
A flicker of a friend does the same,
Up goes another, and down,
Lashing shafts of light into the room.

Up jumps another and another,
Who can jump the highest?
Children dressed in red and yellow
Leaping up.

CLARE TAWNEY, 10
Stoke-on-Trent

The chance

Here I am, lonely in my mother's womb.
As I am lying here, I am wondering
Just whether to come out and see the bright world.
But maybe it is not a bright world,
It's maybe dull, but I can't tell
    if it is a dull world.
I will not be able to get back into the womb
    if it is dull.
It is just a chance I will have to take.

TIMMY CROW, 11
Stepney, London

Oh, poor old Joseph,
You're going away
To a borstal
To be a slave
And bend on your knees
To the police
And say that you love them
Forever more.

But really you hate them,
but you can't say it
or you'll get a kicking
and four years not three,
so what is there to do
for I am a slave
and there is nothing
I can do till the day I leave.

ANITA BURANSKI, 14
Camden Town, London

Why do prices go up and up?
We cannot keep on living.
Why are people so wicked and mean?
We get poorer and poorer every day.
People can't afford
To pay their way.

The rates and taxes are too much to pay.
The people can't afford to pay it all the day.
The parents and children get shabby at times.
But the government are rich and they don't care;
They just quarrel what to wear.

ANDREW CHINN, 9
Tonypandy, Rhondda

My street

My Street is named Sellons Ave.
It is a quiet road.
Different people live in it.
Pakistanis, Coloureds, and Foreign people.
We're all good friends.
We play a lot of football.
Our Mums talk a lot to each other
We usually sit and play records
in each others' houses.
We borrow a lot, sugar, tea, etc.

I have lived in Sellons for all
My life, so far.
So have most of the other boys.

THOMAS O'CONNELL, 13
Harlesden, London

Suburban flashing lights
Confuse and pickle my
Imagination, in an endless
Myriad of discrepancies.

So how, within the barriers of
A mechanized age, can I survive
The wolves that prowl in search
Of food to feed their human greed?

In its confusion, all this
Is real: the power to
Create it all is what
I rely on for my answer.

NICOLA WRIGHT, 17
Oxford

Being poor

Living in a slum,
Wondering where the next meal's coming from,
Freezing in the winter,
No money to buy coal,
Your kids under-nourished,
The floorboards cracking,
Your feet blistered,
Your shoes with holes in the soles,
Watching the rich go by,
Dreaming of winning the pools,
The bills mounting up,
Being poor is a terrible thing.

DESMOND KELLY, 13
Stonebridge, London

Cold, grey bus station,
With cold, grey faces.
Hands in pockets,
Eyes in expressionless faces gazing forward.
Queues of patient, resigned bodies,
Standing carefully apart.
Each thinking their own private thoughts,
In their own private, allotted space.
Separated one from another,
By their own invisible barriers.

Five giggling schoolgirls,
Share a forbidden cigarette,
With frequent anxious glances over shoulders,
United in the delicious sense of guilt.
And in ten years' time,
When we have been moulded,
Into 'mature, responsible adults',
We will stand,
In queues of patient, resigned bodies,
Standing carefully apart.
Each thinking our own private thoughts,
In our own private, allotted space.
Separated one from another,
By our own invisible barriers.

JENNY LEMASURIER, 18
Northampton

10

When they said
'Creepy sideboards are in'
I got them.
When the fashion changed to curls
I managed to grow some.
When plucking your eyebrows was in
I suffered that
And slimmed for weeks
because of Twiggy
only to find that Elizabeth Taylor
had made a come-front.
When shoes were 'pointed-toe'
I had them,
And when they changed
I practised hard and made my feet
'Chunky'.
I was doing very well
Until they switched to
'Barefaced natural look',
When I split down the middle
And flaked away.

ELIZABETH REVELEY, 17
Bradford

11

Knees up Mother Brown

Young boys
Growing up
Learning how to gob properly
Learning how to say eff off
Like Grown-ups do.

Young boys
Who will never grow up to be men
Playing imaginary war games
With imaginary machine-guns
Learn how to die
As in real war games.

Young boys
Daring each other until the devil comes
—It's Tom! they sing: Tom Tom Turnaround, Don't ever
    let me down ...
Laughing until their lemonade lives fizz out of their mouths
When he shouts—
I'll get you!

Running fast out of his way
Giggling
Until his waving fist
And knowledge where they live
Hurts them.

Rollicking on grass
On sunshine each will remember
Shouting beneath the sun
Until their little bodies
Send
For
Sleep.

ANDREW STROWMAN, 18
Bow, London

Dave — the boy who liked to aggravate

Dave walked towards the boy, looking fierce and lean
With eyes looking very mean,
His hair was neatly combed and his trousers were short,
He was ready for bovver of the worst sort.
Dave's eyes were now going thin
And that's when he started to put the boot in.
Dave kicked him very hard and good,
Sometimes he even done it as hard as he could —
Dave left him there covered in blood
He looked very awkward in the mud,
Then after, he went home, cleaned up and picked up a bird
And then he told her the best story she had ever heard.
But that boy's friends waited outside
And when he came out they chased him and he had
   nowhere to hide.
They beat Dave very hard and long
And he was taught to do right, not wrong,
But Dave was already dead
When they laid him on the hospital bed.
So you see it is dangerous to aggravate
Especially if you haven't very tough mates.

LLOYD DOSWELL, 13
Harlesden, London

Children's camp

If enclosed in a field
Are seventy scampering sighing children
Lost to the city's rattling cars
Dragged away from their day-worn metallic cases
Enforced to feel with new natural laws—
Another person, another place,
Another loving
Authority;
If here, pushed intensely, is life
Condensed, all burning feeling
Boiling
To be watched and stirred by the
Teachers
Of society;
If here I find reality
What deceit do I hold.
Come, child, sitting in yellowed grass,
I will not have you suck my breast.
Come, bite my hand with harsh white teeth
Let me know my own red blood
Rippling
On my skin.
Perhaps then I will exist
If you believe me enough
To bite me.
In this place I will work and eat
And forget the streets with you.
For a few days,
While you and this work
Drain me
Of blood and breath
I will not lie.

SYLVIA GIBSON, 17
Chingford

14

The unadopted child

Crash!
Books fly the air,
Toys wrecked,
A chorus of:
'Suzanna, not again!'
Suzanna sits in the corner,
She hides the pain,
Cuddles her teddy bear
'Nobody cares!
All the other children
They've got new mummies,
Why haven't I?
I've waited for three whole years
Nobody wants me, nobody cares!'
Down her cheeks roll the sad tears.
'Nurse, when will I be adopted
And have a home of my own?'
'Maybe tomorrow, dear, we shall see.'
She says in a mournful tone,
'On cuddly six month babies they all
thrive,
But can't they see I need love as well,
I'm alive!
Where are all my aunts and uncles today?
Oh! I forgot,
From big three year old kids like me
They keep at bay.
Soon they are bound to spot me
And if they do,
I hope they will notice I'm rather
pretty too ...
But NO!
I am a girl
When they want a boy,
I am three years old,
When they want a two year old,
I am black
When they definitely want white.
Can I ever win?'

SANDRA HOTENPOW, 13
Edmonton, London

My hero

He's two foot tall,
With boots as big,
His hair's dead short,
He's as thin as a twig,
That's my hero.

He's a skinhead,
He lives in a slum,
His brain is half dead,
They call him the bum,
That's my hero.

He's one of the lads,
A bit of a laugh,
He's football mad,
And wears a blue scarf,
That's my hero.

PETER CLAYTON, 15
Ruislip

Gang slaughter

They dwell on every corner
   lurking in the night,
They wait for violence in anguish,
   the moon to act as light.

They touch their knees in hiding,
   sweat flowing from their hand,
The tension is mounting higher,
   the silence can no longer stand.

The craving for blood has mounted,
   the animal screams in pain,
The gang is sweating lustily,
   a body is torn and slain.

The lust for blood has ended,
   they depart, their job fulfilled,
They leave their victim, unmerciful,
   and vanish while the air is stilled.

IRENE SIMON, 17
Archway, London

I sit and stare
   and long for care
From the cloud man
   In the sky.

I dream and dream
   Of the deep blue stream
That swirls into
   My eye.

HAZEL WEBB, 10
Salisbury

Stronger

Stronger than the sea
My castle's going to be
So that no one needs to save it
My strong little castle for me.

Stronger than the waves my castle's going to be
Like one built of iron
My strong little castle will be
Stronger than the waves.

ZOE DANZIGER, 10
Felixstowe

Far far away
along the mountain side
there's a little town
about 20 foot wide
where no one lives
just you and I
no one lives along the mountain side.

TRACY JONES, 12
Hemel Hempstead

Snowman

Oh, Snowman, Snowman,
so woolly white,
why doesn't it snow for Christmas night?
The icicles hang from tree to tree,
Why doesn't the snow follow me?
When the snow has gone,
and the ice is cracked
We can make a wish in a jumping Jack.
Oh, Snowman, Snowman,
so woolly white,
Why doesn't it snow for Christmas night?

SHARON JOHNSON, 8
Tottenham

Poor child

Poor child
Always playing in muddy puddles
Always getting in scrapes and muddles
Poor child

Poor child
Dirty clothes, dirty hair
Almost always in welfare care
Poor child

Poor child
Living in the dirty slums of a town
When will they ever pull them down
Poor child

Poor child
Will anything ever be done
Will his time ever come
Poor child.

ANONYMOUS, 12
Southwark, London

Young boy's story of the slums

Below the chimney pots
Under the sky
I wonder where in the world am I?

My world is vision
My story one
My hopes, my destiny ...
I must have some.

I have seen lonely looks
And begging faces
And stood alone
In empty places.

Little am I in age
Heavy I rest in thought
Stupid am I in sums
And yet I know
The story of the slums.

ANDREW STROWMAN, 18
Bow, London

the anger was all over my leg
where I was given a kick
I thought the place was burning hot
but all I had was a red patch
the anger filled my heart and my head
I felt the water coming out of my eyes
then all my body was burning like flames
the anger was still in my heart
I thought
I shall kick him back
but I knew I hadn't the guts
the water burst from my eyes
like a burst pipe.

LINDA ROWE, 13
Archway, London

The door

I saw a door.
I tried to open it
but in vain.

I looked for the key.
I saw it up high
I took it down.

But when I got it down
It would not fit
So I pulled the door again.

I fell over.
The door was open.
I looked inside.

I saw a shadow.
I shut the door quickly
And never opened it again.

CATHERINE STEANE, 9
Kettering

I live in a block of flats where people
do play I have no friends day after day
if I have no friend I can't play
so I stay in and look after myself

I noticed they started to talk to
Me it was because I was black
and they were just saying to theirselves, let's speak
Don't be rotten

ANONYMOUS, 14
London

Alone

To be alone is like the closing of a door,
Nothing is heard
No conversation is made
Because there are just ourselves.
To speak of being alone
Is like a cloud of darkness,
The whole room is quiet and still
We miss those who speak to us
For loneliness deserves company.

SHARON JOHNSON, 13
Tottenham, London

I walked along a solitary road
and did not hear a sound
apart from steps that were my own
falling upon the ground

a great tree twisted to the sky
and as I passed that silent tree
I heard the singing sailor sing

I passed the tree and heard no more
the singing sailor sing
the road looked like
a curl of smoke
in the light
of the moon

MARTHA CHARALAMBOUS, 15
Holloway, London

My hero

My hero is D. Dougan,
He wears old gold and black.
He goes through all defenders,
He leads the Wolves attack.

He scores in nearly every game,
He thrills the north bank choir.
He kicks the ball right through the net,
Just like a ball of fire.

JOHN LANE, 12
Cannock

The Ibrox disaster

It was Hogmanay
When everybody doesn't go to work
    for a week,
They just get drunk
They fight, till they fall.
Then came the climax of the week—
RANGERS v. CELTIC,
The two best teams in Scotland.
All was well at half-time,
RANGERS 0 CELTIC 0,
The fans were happy
And drunk.
Then one minute from time
A Celtic attack built up,
A shot from a Celtic player
Crashed against the crossbar,
Then as the ball rebounded into play
    with the goalkeeper helpless,

26

A Celtic player called Jimmy Johnstone
  headed it into the net.
Then the whole stadium exploded,
The Celtic fans went mad,
Certain for victory,
The Rangers fans started to go home
With thinking of defeat.
Then as the crowd moved away
With ten seconds to go,
Rangers scored with a free kick
  from Colin Stein.
The Rangers fans that were leaving
  heard a roar,
Then a little boy who was leaving the stadium
Ran up to the top of the steps—
'They've scored, Rangers have scored.'
As he turned round
He pulled his coat over his head
And fell back down the steps.
As he struggled to get up
The Rangers fans tried to get back to see,
But then it happened
So quick
People toppling over
Just like that.
A barrier broke—
People
Squashed, Crushed, Suffocated to death
Just like that.
As they laid the bodies on the pitch
It looked more like a cemetery …

PETER   KETT, 15
Holloway, London

The adoration of the idolts

Booted feet and clipped-down hair,
Feel a need to go and scare
Everything and everyone,
And that's your idea of fun.

You gain the adoration of the idolts,
'Isn't he good,
Just like everyone should
Always be,
Isn't he tough,
Isn't he rough,
That's what we can see.'

Kicking a sphere are twenty-two
Men with nothing better to do,
Trying to get a ball in a net
Doesn't ever impress me yet.

They gain the adoration of the idolts,
'What a save,
What a close shave
From scoring,
What a good goal,
They're taking their toll
Of the other side, as the rain is pouring.'

Lazing back and acting like fools,
Ignoring all of the rules,
Never showing any concern,
But will they ever learn?

But they gain the adoration of the idolts,
'Aren't they a laugh,
Yes, not half,
They are such fun
Aren't they a scream?'
Are they as funny as they seem,
Has the fun just begun?

Idolts
Standing everywhere,
Idolts
All just stand and stare,
Idolts
Everywhere,
There and there and there and there.

KEVIN HEWICK, 14
Leicester

Facts and fantasy

I dream about the wedding,
Fantasy of course,
But a wedding is coming soon—
Fact this time.

Fantasy is so unreal
But it's nice to dream
Fact puts the truth to you
So it's quite cruel.

People escape to fields of fantasy
Because they can't face the truth,
But, never mind, the time will come
For them to see the facts.

Life flies past in a world of fantasy,
But in fact it goes quite slow,
So why dream of fantasy
When you have to see the truth some day.

SANDRA BALLOCH, 15
Stepney, London

I walked on the clouds
but they melted
And I fell like rain
I touched the wet naked sky and painted
it many colours
with moods and hues
I touched the tips of skyscrapers
That come like icebergs
Into the sky
And let the people trapped
Beneath the concreteglass
FREE
eventually I landed on brown soggy earth
And walked away.

TERESA NOWELL, 15
Barnet

The river

The sun is shining on
the river
The water flowing with a
shiver
Round the winding lanes
I go
The sun has gone the
winds blow
The river goes on past
the trees
Carrying papers carrying leaves
I'm getting nearer to the
sea
I'm going on feeling
free.

LYNNE DOLAN, 11
Liverpool

Waking

At first awareness of dawn
the sky opens,
a spectrum streaking over.

And as a bird rises
soaring over deserted suburbia
I notice a man with a gun, aiming.

The day unwinds.

STEPHEN CRICK, 14
Kingston-upon-Thames

Sunrise on the water

The wind is calm
The water is calm
Rippling gently
Like a psalm,
The sun is going down
It looks as if it's skimming the water
Gently, gently skimming the water.

MICHELE QUIGLEY, 9
Notting Hill, London

Roomful of shadows

I stood in a roomful of shadows,
Silent,
Waiting,
For myself.

I stood in a roomful of mirrors,
Moving,
Looking,
For myself.

I stood in a roomful of light.
Blinking,
Smiling,
For myself.

PETER CUNNINGHAM, 15
Jersey

Using my frame of mind to border my imagery

In streets of night,
I walk alone,
Everywhere the lamp post lights
Had grown.
I walked upon reflections
And reflected as I walked,
Trees looked plastic,
Road drains talked.
On a battlement wall
Shone an orange light,
A ray of hope in a
Concrete night;
And the real looked false,
The false looked real,
The dim looked bright,
The bright looked pale.
Still the rain continued to fall and the
Colours of the night all ran into the gutter.

MICHAEL LYNCH, 16
York

Night

As I lie alone, thinking, meditating on this peace,
across the path of imagination,
curves a certain calm.

I look outside and see a house
black silhouette in the clear sky.
And at some far distance a bark,
sound, fading into the night.

Staring upwards I see a star,
quivering, out of my reach.
I think, surely there is something more
than just me,
my small unimportant life.
Surely, there is more to it than that.

Up there, in that forbidden veil
there must be a destiny,
something to aim for.

And I know, that even if it is only me,
that I am going to stretch for that future
lost in the middle
of the dark curve.

STEPHEN CRICK, 14
Kingston-upon-Thames

35

Night poem

Your petals
blow across my windscreen.
Scarlet moons
dance like reeling blossom.
Your picture
radiates through my night.
Your heart
beats in my dim obscurity.

But when the dawn aches
into the naked day.

In an empty Woolworth's you
stand
behind a cluttered counter
selling
Plastic Petals on Plastic moons
your
Plastic Picture stains the light
and your
Plastic heart stops, when I
see you
in the Halo of day.

MARTEN CLIBBENS, 15
Wantage

Death in the Cairngorms

They started off one afternoon
The wind was blowing cold
All eight were in the flower of youth
But all of them were bold

They wrapped up warm and off they went
And found the mountains high,
With tired feet they plodded on
And cloudy grew the sky.

'My God, the wind is blowing up
I think we must turn back.'
'It's only a short mountain storm
We'll shelter in the shack.'

The wind howled loud throughout the night
And battered on the door.
One teacher said, 'Don't be afraid,'
As they huddled on the floor.

'Tomorrow we shall soon return
Into the valley warm
Or else a mountain team will come
And rescue us from harm.'

Foolish were the parents
To let their children climb
They sit alone in their empty homes
And drown their thoughts in wine.

Eventually the bodies were found
Frozen to the marrow
Luckily two were still alive
But they also felt the sorrow.

Now let this be a warning
To all those who wish to climb
That cold and snow are killers,
And that is not so fine.

SIMON CROWE AND FRIENDS, 12
Worcester

Time and distance
They both travel equally
Waiting for no one
Time is sometimes wasted
Time is sometimes fastened
The green grass is taken by time
    as time goes into the future
And makes it present and the grass
    is polluted.
Sometimes people are left behind
    by time, when people are old
    the time leaves them.
The world and its people get old
But time goes on and on.

INTIAZ MALEK, 14
Stepney, London

The Earth drags on, heavier and heavier by the ever growing
    population,
Our star begins to lose its shine,
Grandfather's clock ticks on leaving its owner to rot.
No one wants to wait, listen and look at themselves or what
    they are doing to what is around them.
At last they become old and slow and are left behind by the
    new generation,
Like a new bulb from an old powerhouse.

INTIAZ MALEK, 14
Stepney, London

The Sun shone through the open window
To pack the world with a closed-in atmosphere.
The room, tense and weird, stood shaking,
Then dissolved into a thousand pieces of
Matter
Only to be picked up and put into place
           like a giant jigsaw
Growing smaller each time till the end of
      TIME.

LESLEY SAMUELS, 12
Stepney, London

Royal Mint Square

The dark and dreary place
Pulled down from existence,

Its happy sparks nearing the dynamite

Old people dying
With this unhappy world of Royal Mint Square.

The merciless dynamite explodes
Pulling the body of the square apart.

INTIAZ MALEK, 14
Stepney, London

Death

Why don't I cry?
Surely this grave deserves my scarlet-sad tears.

The death of a friend
like a black sun that melts
into the morning.

STEPHEN CRICK, 14
Kingston-upon-Thames

The day our dog died

It was Sunday morning when I awoke
To see the face of my mum.
She, her eyes full of tears, said
Softly, unsteadily, 'She ... She's
Gone in her sleep.'
I felt upset, yet in a way
Happy—
For she was blind and almost deaf
But full of life.
It seemed a cruel kind of thing,
Like one of the family had died.
I waited until my mum had gone,
And for a while cried.
I went downstairs, my head aching
And my dog gone.

RAMONA HARRIS, 11
Stepney, London

Rain on the graves

I go to school in a car each morning;
Today it is raining
Raining on the graves.
Rain on the graves;
It is a beautiful sight.
It gives me a funny feeling
To think of layers of corpses
Waiting, waiting for the time when they must wake.
Some have crosses
Some have stones
Some have plain grass graves
Some have boxes grey and rectangular.
Some are ashes
Some are skeletons.
People have died there
Good people for bad reasons.
Some of the graves are battered and broken;
People lie in the damp earth
Helpless and sleeping
Like a layer of waiting fighters
Ready to fire.
Prisoners of death, they are crying for light.
O I can't describe the feeling it gives me
To see rain on the graves.

ALLISON DYER, 9
Halstead

Hot, red wax

I recoiled at the sudden
shock
of the candlewax.
It hardened red,
as congealed blood,
and burnt my little finger,

When I peeled away this man-made crust
thoughts of bleeding,
blood
and sighing
the nails hammered through Christ's hands
clutched at my skin
and tore a hole, a gap,

I hid inside myself
to escape the reddish, sullen flicker
which lit the face of my sad death
outlined in hot, red wax.

DAVID LEWIS, 16
Scarborough

Troubles

I said goodbye to all of them last night.
They none of them realized that the sight
Of the smoke-begrimed train
Would be their last of me;
That they would not meet me until they, too,
Had come to see me here within my room.

A small room, this new room of mine,
Through two murky panels there shines
A diffused and useless light,
Only for this one night;
For which I shall rend, cut and tear
The sheets, to stop cracks cheating me.

But troubles will pass barriers,
Find those who only closed their ears
To my lone sensitivity—
I, the lost one, feel, living like
The lamb, my parent flock now turned to wolves.
I spend my shillings, and relish choking
By happiness.

PETE BERNARD, 17
Hornchurch

Laugh with the crowd

When you see
On your TV
Death from war,
Or starving millions,
Do you just forget
Soon after?

Do you go away
And begin to play
Your silly games?

Well, if you can laugh,
Go and laugh with the crowd,
But if you can cry
Go and cry all alone.

When you sleep
Do you keep
Seeing the faces
Of the poor and dead,
Or do you dream
Of fairy tales?

Do you know it,
Or does your mind flit
To something else?

Well, if you can laugh,
Go and laugh with the crowd,
But if you can cry
Go and cry all alone.

KEVIN HEWICK, 14
Leicester

The Bengal disaster – East Pakistan

Death
Is swatting the flies of hunger
As they come to rest on the worries
Of five continents.
Cholera spreads through the Englishman's breakfast
And the pangs of imagined hunger
Cross his gout-ridden belly.

The six o'clock thriller?
Robert Dougal.
Television monochrome turning
Fact into Fiction
In alarming technicolour.

Knitting squares for the blankets of
Hope,
Charity workers converse,
Bullied together into tight embryos of industry
By shocking realization of
Life.

Life and its Deaths.

DEBORA COOMBS, 14
Southampton

Still life: child's body in water
(East Pakistan)

The opaque surface,
the dirty water takes away
the sunlight's silly
laughter,
    absorbs the rills and childish
ripples in its drab solemnity—
    slugging sullen 'neath
the dead ashed sky,
heaving huge sigh sometimes
that tells the holy boredom
of raped elements.

    The wind has whipped away
the youth in this land,
torn apart the very flesh of
colour, and the rain has
picked its bones.

    United now in
apathy aftermath
of war with the cyclone—
the unwitting creation of
these three—

fused in fog—the sea and sky,
clamped in mud—the sea and land,
and denounced—
the religion of the instigator
sun.

In the water, eyes down
still clear to the dirt,
looking down a muddy eternity
to a source whose little light
lies always trembling just behind—
    raped of colour
    raped of a gleam in the
corners of an eye,

raped of movement, the clutch
of a baby treasure more
secret than life —
the sobobbing body
of a weightless child turns slow
to the
North,
South,
East,
and lastly to the West,
asking not a thing of the
weeping world.

TERRY EDGE, 18
Upminster

So misunderstood

I was a tree upon a hill
I was a tree upon a hill
looming, high, over lost faces,
and I remembered how the thorns bit my skin,
how the ropes burnt my wounds.

There was a music,
a bloody, numbing music.
Their sins I eased with my tears.

None pitied my broken body,
it snapped under the weight of my shaft.

I was your tree upon a hill
I was your tree upon a hill

DAVID LEWIS, 16
Scarborough

I once saw a man in Nazareth.
He was born in a stable.
Now, two thousand years later,
That man has caused poverty,
Not able,
Not able to see what he has caused
Or who has suffered for him—
But when palaces rot and children cry,
Who then will carry that cross?
Not him.

Money and government shelter this man,
For churches must rot without it—
And remember who caused that man's terrible death,
Now it's us that carry the cost.

Though, when I complain,
I still feel the pain
For others that are paying the cost,
One day I will be able to say,
'You're not the only one
            on that cross.'

KIM OAKES, 13
Clerkenwell, London

The face from outer space

A face from outer space
Came down from the sky
And he was all slimy
And he was all sly.

And he had no mouth
And a flat nose
And big round eyes
And hair made out of barbed wire.

And I saw him come
From the sky
And I ran and ran
And I saw a helicopter.

When I got in
There was no petrol
The monster was getting closer
And closer and ...

Bang
It blew up
Killing me and the monster
That was its end
Its face was splattered.

DAVID APPLETON, 14
Durham

Run behind the face

A mask to show
You're
A nice man.
Run behind the face
Nice man:
The plastic smile
While your murders breed.
Is it the sincerity mask
Nice man?
This afternoon
When your gas-meter chat flows
Are the old ladies
Taken in neatly
Nice man?
And when mister policeman comes
Are you an honest man
Nice man?
If an innocent man threatens
Are you a tough man
Nice man?
Tinker? Tailor? Soldier? Sailor?
Nice man?

VIRGINIA BYFIELD, 13
Reading

Ghosts

I got off my horse as I shivered in the dark
My hands chattered at the door
My horse's hooves clumped on the muddy slimy floor
I said, 'Who's there, you asked me to call
So here I am, what do you want?'
All I heard was whispering
All I heard was spiders talking
So I quietly got on my horse
And galloped away.

JENNY WAITE, 8
East Sheen

Dream of fear

The night is silent,
But for the trees
Whispering,
And my heart at my knees
Knocking.
The moon has taken on
A shape of knowing,
Its dim light bestowing
And growing all the time.
Where is my confidence,
I only feel fear,
And my pulse rate jumps
As something brushes past my ear.
I fall to the ground
And close my eyes,
For the trees are closing in on me
With fangs of greed,
Taking seed
In my flesh.
Then I scream, and suddenly
I am awake,
And only the ceiling looms over me.

NIKOLA GREENFIELD, 15
Shaftesbury

Amnesia

A voice calls
I clear my brain
a lily white hand
soothes away all pain
'don't cry my child'
all pain is past
don't look at them
in sorrow
at the last
'You have won through.'
'Are you an angel,
You must be mad
I can't be here
I've been so bad
but at the end I prayed
but not for me, so why have I been saved?'
'My child, you dreamed your death
and slept on through destructions
you prayed before you slept,
You have five minutes to the end of time.'

GILLIAN P., 14
Durham

Fear

It came nearer and nearer;
I could even see
The white of its eyes.
It was grinning at me.
Whatever it was I didn't know about it.
I could see the whipper-snapping teeth,
Its jaws were wide open
Its claws fully flushed.
With head down
I was screaming
Without the scream
Crying
Without the tears
Scared beyond belief.
I felt that I was
Absolutely insane.
One claw came down
Then the other
Then the teeth snapped
A tail sent me flying ...
Then I fell out of bed
And woke up.

ROBERT LEWIS, 14
Durham

The man who hated himself

He drew pictures of himself
And threw darts at the pictures
He hated him
He would look in a mirror
And begin to hate him more
He really hated him
He really loathed him.
One day while walking
He saw his reflection
in a pool
so he killed him.

JIMMY, 14
Durham

The extinct life

He sat by the window
Deep in the night
The silence was pierced
A distant soothing tune cutting through the dark
Still smog ran in his ears.
He was nearing a broken road now
A deep hole, an eternal hole
Which he would not pass to reach his destination.

INTIAZ MALEK, 14
Stepney, London

The hate makers

They make you hate people
Who are 'they'?
They're the hate makers from a different galaxy
They slip tablets in your food which drive you
To hate people.
Why?
Nobody knows
Who?
Nobody knows
Nobody knows who or why.
The hate makers
You get locked up if you hate people
I hate the hate makers ...
......
Don't say that—you'll be locked up.

JIMMY MANSON, 14
Kilmarnock

Elders and betters

I have my Elders and Betters,
Aunts, Uncles, Mum, Dad and Cousins.
If I had to honour all these
My life would be like in a cage.
The bars would be made from
Must, Shoulds and Obeys.
Oh how can I think of my Elders
In these ways?

JEAN JOSEY
Reading

Parents

Wrinkled with inside knowledge,
Wise old man
Born before death.
I emerge into the new world
In which I myself am new.
The old man from his mother's womb
Loses his age
And begins a new life
The blur which was my father
Slowly takes shape.
The chest which was my mother
Grows up to a head,
And down to legs and feet.
I begin to notice details
That I hadn't noticed before.
Bald head
Grey and white hair.

In later life
The shapes distort yet again.
This time it is not my own eyes.

SIMON DAVIES, 13
Canterbury

59

My father. Tears in yer beer

A cosy pub
with people pulling faces,
making actors with their eyes
and always saying here
I am I am me and I am real.
Alone like a sculpture
in your sympathetic chair,
you ponder just the same
as granite does
alone in midnight
galleries
with only paint and
frigid hearts
to find him company.
   You ponder light
and how it touches off
all kinds of unsuspecting
things;
bubbles in your beer
fall slowly upwards
blank-faced in their
gravity-blasphemy,
and in the
topsy-turvy glass you're
upside down,
your marble mouth
is smiling at you,
so you smile too,
and the sarcastic bulbs
reverse your feeling
with all the whimsy of
scientific light;
   and then pondering
comes too ponderous
and hanging head away
from
all the level-headed
beams upon you,
folding up inside like
so much bubbles,

you shed a
little light of your own,
a little light
for no one else
but her.

TERRY EDGE, 18
Upminster

Love could have given life

He needed life
But more than life, needed understanding;
It was up to him,
How could he swim
When he was always drowning?

His parents thought they knew
All the art of living,
But how could that be true
When they were never giving?

People asked him why he took the stuff,
He looked at them and said:
'I've never seen the good side of living
So what's it like to be dead?'

I wonder what his teachers thought,
'Extremely intelligent'
'Has a mind all of his own'
'A future William Blake!'
He went along his narrow life
Paying for one mistake.

ANDREW STROWMAN, 18
Bow, London

61

In my mother's house

I am within your womb of ambition,
Your dreams, schemes, enclose me now
The warmth of your life's painful conclusion
Is what I suck of now.
A drop of your blood
Womb-blood, now conceives its
Own frantic worrying.
Taking of you
A squeeze, a careful globe of pin-pricked pain,
Has burst the boundaries of your womanhood
To cut, and cut again,
With its departure taking more
That its own particles
Breaking the darkened clots that protect you,
To make you bleed again.
And pour out new life.
My life.
I gorge myself
Selfness feeding,
Knowing I will never feed again
And sup on richness so freely given,
Or so easily drained.

SYLVIA GIBSON, 17
Chingford

62

Mamoushka (my mother)

Mamoushka lies
flat out
on the beach,
loved by many
selecting few.
Body caressed
by the wind
and the sand,
hair blowing wildly
in the gentle breeze
while tanning like a ripe nut
to a dark brown
in the afternoon sun.
She is healthy
from indulging only in simple
pleasures like
good food
plenty of exercise
little wine
good music and books,
to name but a few.
She floats in water
and in dreams,
spending her time
wandering on the shore
childishly,
pebble collecting.

SINNET KABRAJI, 17
Tunbridge Wells

My parents

Just a simple ode
To some simple folk
A good hearted lady
And a decent bloke.

Their sacrifices have been big
The returns very small
Have given all their love
And regretted nothing at all.

How do I know? Well I should you see
Because I am the daughter
Praising the folk
Who have looked after me.

ANGELA TATHAM, 16
Stratford, London

My father makes a steam engine

My father is making a steam engine. He has made one
  steam engine
but it is too small to ride on.
The first steam engine is finished.
The name of the steam engine is Doris.
It took him three or two years to make the steam engine.
My Dad made a set to fix on the back of the steam engine.
Sometimes I sit on the back of the steam engine.
I have to pull myself along.
The steam engine can go on its own.
My Dad is planning on to sell the first steam engine.
When the second steam engine is finished he is going to
  make
tracks up and down the garden.
This is a true story.

JOSEPHINE HALL, 13
Burton-upon-Trent

My parents

My Dad comes in,
Sats down,
Shouting at my Mum,
He gets up,
For his pipe,
He comes back to put the
tele on,
He sats down,
Puffing away,
He puts his pipe out,
And gets his dinner,
Comes back,
Sats down,
And goes to bed.

ROY CATTLE, 14
Ipswich

My parents

They gave me life
Can it be that what I am
Is theirs?
They cannot know my thoughts and hopes
And fears.

They gave me life,
Yet all I am is mine
Not theirs.
I've lived within my self alone
For years.

They gave me life
To run and think and grow my way
Not theirs.
Now can I give to them my happiness
Not tears.

MARK VINTEN, 10
Ashford, Kent

My parents

Black and white
Who came together to form the unthinking greyness of a
    child
A child that grew as me.
I was the uncoloured creature of the two,
Of the white
Who nursed me at her breast
And fed me
And gave me of herself
That I might live.
The loving white who taught me all the things that I should
    know
And nurtured me, and brought my mind to seed.
But in this teaching grace, she turned me
And made me know the black, the all-consuming black
Who taught that he was right and I was wrong
And told me I must love the black and white
The tender white and black
Who came together in love and shut me out
To touch me by the circle of their love
And not the heart
I loved the black and white, until I realized they shut me out
Until I saw
Among the muted clearness of dark and light
The strange and tainted grey
The grey that as a child I left behind
That filthy grey that I had seen in others
But never in my black and white.
Forgive me, for I cannot love the grey
It makes me flinch
And cry out in my love to see again
That first enticing colour of their souls
But this is not to be
For now I see them as I see myself
Outside the blinding circle of their love.

MARGARET PULLAR, 16
Edinburgh

Miracles

Mum, if I could work miracles,
I would work one just for you.
We know you've worked hard
To bring us up right—
That's for sure,
What with Daddy being sick
We have been very poor.

But still we are happy
Despite the dismal gloom

But God knows there will come a day
When we all shall feel the ...
BOOM

TONY HUSSEY, 13
Spitalfields, London

My mother worked
In a laundry,
Long ago
When she was young.
Then my Mother
Left the laundry,
And married
My first Dad.
They worked
In lots of clubs
Until dad died.
My new dad
Is a sailor
In the Merchant Navy.
My new dad sails
To all different places.
He brings me
Toys and different things.
He gives me
Pocket money
To buy sweets.
I do not see
Much of him though.

DEBORAH GOLDIE, 9
Wakefield

'Your mam and me are going out,
So you stay in, don't muck about.'
The door slams loudly in my face
To get to the pub they must race.
All life is to them is gamble and beer,
So they live up the town
While I'm waiting here.

BILLY CARSON, 12
Silsden

Old age

Age, gradually creeps
Overtakes and sleeps
Creaking old bones
Damp, lonely homes
Age
Shut up in a cage
Like animals, lonely and scared
With no one to care
No one there
Old Age.

SALLY BEALE, 13
Limpley Stoke

sitting on a bus
an old man cries
cries away his age
his dirt
his 'beer and ten whiffs please'
his late wife
better without her life
shame at tears
producing more
than his withered old body
should hold
crying his oneness
solemnness
even Christmas
brought no life to him.
Old man, don't cry!
lest you begin
what men should have done
many years ago
and the dust will be kept down
by men's tears.

GILLIAN P., 14
Durham

Nobody cared

The tramp lay on an old park bench,
With stubbly chin and unkempt hair,
Unwashed for weeks — you could tell
                    by the stench —
Covered with newspaper,
And nobody cared.

The factory effluent poured into the river,
Killing all life between there and the sea.
The dying young salmon gave one last shiver,
And lay dead in the shallows,
And nobody cared.

The world was dying.
The rot had set in.
No one could stop it, and nobody tried,
Because nobody cared.

ARCHIE CAMPBELL, 13
Inverness

Spinning a record

Tonight
I heard a Cockney say
I can hold eight pints
And his mate, say,
Get away!

Today front page
I saw a front-page story in a local paper:
'A DOCKER'S SON CAN DROWN A PINT IN 2 SECONDS.'

This morning
This afternoon
This evening.
The disrespected dosser will beat
Any record for alcoholic consumption

But Guinness will never put him in their year book
Nor my local paper boast him in bold captions.

Skipper, how much is a medal worth these days?

ANDREW STROWMAN, 18
Bow, London

The busker

Everywhere. People pushing, shoving, poking,
Violently.
Made it seem as if all the world was there that day.
Yet all were wrapped up in their shells
—Unaware of each other—
—Unaware of themselves.

So, the man on the corner,
Despite his outlandish clothes
Was by-passed by all,
Noticed by none.

Standing there alone
The features of his face
Half-distinguishable in that misty light,
His face concentrating on his hands,
For in those hands was the glowing butt of his last cigarette.

From underneath his arm he pulled a violin,
And in a slow and gentle manner began to play.
Oblivious of all around he began his song ...
The notes hung in the still grey air.

A harsh note echoed down the street,
Destroying the magic of the scene,
A penny shone coppery-silver in the half-light.
It rolled to his feet.

He did not stoop to pick it up—
He did not lower himself.

MAURA DOOLEY, 15
Bristol

My hero

A stream of silk milk
Flows through his mind river
Words, sounds, meanings, feelings
Tossing and touching.
Dead
But not dominated.
Rushing timble words
Spill out of a beer bottle.

Desire of pureness
Groping, searching
Pursuing the whole.
Undominated
Dead.

LYNNE HUGHES, 17
St Albans

The old man I like very much

The old man I like very much
I met on holiday last year
He could do tricks
And he said crusts made your hair curly
And he peeled potatoes sitting on the steps that went up to
    the barn
With his dogs roaming round early in the morning before
    breakfast.

RACHEL JENKINS, 8
Hitchin

Loneliness

I, the lonely dustman, go walking along the dusty streets,
    my only truthful friends are the rubbish.
They come rushing against me, so that I can throw my
    only friends away into a world of rubbish.
Every day my friends are thrown into the streets and put
    into iron cages,
And they rely on me to take them out of a dreadful, dirty
    and awkward world of horror.
Then along comes a different world.
It's a dust-cart.
Then once more my friends rush against me and I throw
    them into a world of darkness.
But now we are on strike, I see my friends wherever I go.

MAXINE LOFTUS, 11
Stepney, London

The nightwatchman

He sits shivering, rubbing his hands over the dying fire,
A grizzled man,
With no visible personality.
He sits like a statue, all through the night,
Every night.
With envious eyes he views the homegoers.
His only companions: the church clock
Speaking every half-hour, and the moon,
Shining, but dumb.
He is the lonely lord of the night.

ROSALIND STONE, 11
Sanderstead

Bill the ferryman

Bill the ferryman knows the river like a seagull,
In the misty mornings he just drives, just as though it
    wasn't misty.
When the snow is on the ground
And the wide world around us is white,
He drives the ferry day and night.
The R.A.F. men get off the ferry in the morning,
And when the day is just dawning.

GEORGINA EMMOTT, 10
Bawdsey Island, Suffolk

Soliloquy in the park

Thin and gaunt now,
faded and pale.
The girl hunts under benches
and around trees
for her far off dreams.

Deceiving herself
she stoops, kneels to pick a
dandelion.
This girl is plucking dandelions
from her past.

She grasps her flowers
with a despairing love.
Caressing her bouquet,
she sits amongst the buzz of a
summer
she once knew,
and kisses her flowers;
as her smiles reflect
around the park.

But her mortal eyes stray to an alien sign;

'KEEP OFF THE GRASS'

She remembers her days of
keeping off,
and a tear falls as she
drowns in the grass,
cast upon a reef of dandelions.

MARTEN CLIBBENS, 15
Wantage

Surbiton woman

Shuffling and shambling
In her odd, broken gait,
Her eyes flash madly
And her fingers twitch;
Her body is jerked from
One step to another,
And the people pass by
They don't say a word.

The little black dog
Is one friend by her side,
The two walk together,
Both in the leaves.

Where are they going?
To sit in the park?
The trees are trained there,
And the flowers grow tall;
There are notices everywhere,
And polite people stare.
Those people smile,
And then whisper when she's gone.

And me,
What do I do?
I stand at the bus stop:
Communication fails.
I'm just like all the rest,
Except in small details.

ROBERT SEATTER, 15
Surbiton

My teacher

Her hair is like smog clinging to a building
Her eyes are like death's army marching
towards me.
And her teeth are like jagged rocks,
devouring ships.
Her nose is like a blunt pencil.

JACINTA DAY, 10
Wigan

'Safely educated' – by an average child

A silence curled, fleshy and cold,
unfolding in the fragrance of a stillborn flower
in the chalky air.
We tried to speak and cut our words in the
desk-shaped trees
but the words that we saw were new,
so the books on the shelves with their smelly breath
shook their heads,
and the silence grew.

CHRISSY WEBBER, 16
Seaford

My teacher

(This poem is in reverse, from my teacher to me, or the way I would feel, if I were a teacher, about pupils that had long since left school)

If you were to wake
away from sudden dreams,
would you, in that future darkness,
remember me?
In the nightness like an
unanswered prayer,
when your wife is not there
to help you
but travelling miles away
in impossible lands
right in the very bed,
the very grave of your childhood,
trampling the wreaths
of your memories,
will you think of me?
Will you be frightened at
the silence in
your bedroom tomb
and seek for sucklers
in the bosoms of the past?
   I will not be there—
somewhere where the
rainbow joins hands
with the sea
and the cliff crumbles
with the strain
of the sky,
   you will find me,
flittering, spinning
around the shapeless clouds
and wishing for stars
to jiggle with.
   Turn back to sleep then,
and dream of my
torture.

84

Be blessed with a
nightmare of lost
causes, broken toys
and
unfair maturities.
Then awake
with no memory
but a piece of
your heart gone
and turn to your
wife to
mend it anew.

I'm too far away
and impossible now.

TERRY EDGE, 18
Upminster

Exam
Red warning lights flash.
Facts
Rattle into my head
Like empty tin cans,
Stuck like thorns
A needle in the eye
And wondering
Why.
Memory bank.

Fear
The vault seals.
Start
The heathen ritual begins
Again
The screw tightens
Nerves twitch to life
The brain clogs
Distorts with mental strife.
Panic

Confusion
Whirlpools drown my brain.
Remember
Myriads of identical keys
Which one?
The time sands sift.
Rusty cogs and spindles turn
A dizzy merry-go-round of facts,
A blur.
Misery.

Write
Scrawp flesh from bone.
Time
The seconds race
Decaying stars in my head;
Forgetting all
That was never learnt.
Splinters of knowledge
Cracked and burned
Stampeding.

Think
A spark glides.
Stop
The paper dissolves
Like another bad dream,
Ever unwritten words
Haunting
Chained release,
A petal floating
Mindache.

VALERIE LEYFIELD, 16
Upton-by-Chester

Before an examination

Pausing for a moment
From the world's giddy flight,
I chance a brief look at
The stars' panorama
The winking universe
Of blinking points of light,
And see that Man beholds
A tiny mite of all
Creation in his eye.

I see the pettiness
Of gods who ask so plain
Of callow youthfulness
To tell in just three hours
How blinding history failed.
Come the millennium
The answer may be called:
Who made the dusty cloud
Of which the earth was formed?

PAUL FOX, 18
Chesterfield

Three more years!
My shaking hand will grasp my pen
And frantically scribble.
The sweat will flow as fast as ink
In nervous desperation.

Pass or fail?
I'll scan the list to find my name,
The worst I'll be expecting.
Now will a college be my fate?
Or National Assistance?

JEAN WATSON, 13
Grimsby

I am one of those Secondary Moderners,
The ones that the future holds nothing in store for,
Don't anyone tell me I have a future,
Because I am one of a million fleas
Trapped in a land of giant bees.
When I left school my heart was set on writing,
When I left school I didn't know that all my life I'd be
    fighting.
Something called a working man's ditch,
Where the poorer get poor and the richer get rich.
Already my bones begin to ache
And my mind is drugged to hell with all the trash of life,
    my life,
Already at seventeen my soul begins to stretch and awake,
And I wish with all my brain,
I could go back to sleep again.

Future, Bah,
What future have I?
I'll tell you what the fruitful 'Garden of Eden' has for me,
To exist in a ball of confusion and constant delusion, and
    die.
But if I could choose my destiny.
If but, by a little bit of luck, I could see where I'm going
My eyes would see a class of writer, of that of Mark Twain,
I would for the children of the earth such colourful figures
My pen would paint, and for all people I would create
Such dreams my mind does weave
My hands do feel, my heart does grieve
Never to write such stories.
My future, is long drowning years
All made up of eight hours, five days, and holidays of one
    week or two
I must go on, plodding on with the broken spirits,
The wild and the meek, the strong and the weak,
This then is my future.

PETER GRESTY, 17
Chadderton

90

I am going to the Grammar School
Oh! my first day
You get a lot of homework there,
To last you one whole day,
Playing football,
This will be great fun,
They say there's a gymnasium there
But I don't care,
I've come to work,
To get 'O' levels,
Working all the time,
We'll start half an hour before nine.

WAYNE GRAHAME, 9
Mexborough

The walls of the classroom quietly crumble

The master breathes up deeply and sighs at the class.
Silence falls again.
The silence closes in and presses hard against the ears of
    the class.
Everyone stared into space ...
Embarrassment fell in a red film down the master's face.
He coughed and tried again:
'Twenty-six point three multiplied by the sum of sixty-two
    ... Oh God!'
He sank back in his chair.
The class stared glassy-eyed, silent, still.
Then music started.
The class and master listened. A beautiful love story drifted
    over.
The walls of the classroom quietly crumbled.

CLIVE DAVIES, 13
Reading

My teacher sat there
  when we come in.
We get on with our work
  why do we work for him?
He sat there playing around
  why can't we play around
Like he do?
  He play like a little baby
Why can't we play like a baby
  like he do?
He make aeroplanes and fly them
  around.
Why can't we play around like he do?
  When he play he make us work
While he play with aeroplanes
  like a little baby.

GLENN NOLLOTH, 14
Ipswich

My teacher

She stares at me
With glaring eyes,
'Why were you late,
Come here' she cries.

My hand out stretched,
Out comes her cane,
A short sharp rap,
And then the pain.

She has brown hair,
Like greasy chips,
A long white face,
And thin pale lips.

ROSEMARY PROOM, 11
Sutton, Surrey

My teacher

He lives in a decrepit house.
That stands alone
Undetached to all but him.
He comes to school
In the early dawn
His hands shaking
His face dull
Mumbling at a girl
that passes by.
His eyes screw
As the bell rings
The children's shouts
Turn to dead silence
As he slumps into the bare classroom.
The bare desks
In the same old lines
The cane beside him
Which everyone knows too well.
For a long half hour he writes.
We look at the board
Another day's work begins.

DAVID BUTCHER, 11
Ravenshead

My teacher

Teacher, Teacher who are you,
Sitting on that chair so tall,
Tell me your name and what do you teach,
Also pray tell me what do you eat?

Many people sit and stare
Watching your face with its frightening glare
Ranting and Raving all day long
Not giving a thought to those who stare.

Teacher, Teacher who are you
Sitting on that chair so tall
Do you really cane, cook, eat and digest people?
If so your mind is wanted elsewhere.

SHARON SUSAN DAY, 13
Finchley, London

My teacher

The world moves slower here,
and sultry droning dies in silence.
The faded light of tired afternoon
Seeps through the greying clouded glass
and falls in golden puddles on his desk.

'Why can't you see beyond these four
dejected walls?
Why can't you see the glorious past?
Life is a dream, which you cannot
yet dream;
You only show the musty dust of books
and think of things you know can never
last.'

The old man sits at his woodwormed desk,
Distracted, thinking,
In long-lost mines of antiquated glory
Sinking.

MATTHEW FRANCIS, 14
Woking

A teacher read,
He read on and on
About colour,
I just glared
The period ended
He demanded to know what I was
        glaring at,
I told him
I was admiring his arctic colour.
He glared more,
And shouted me down to the head.
The head quietly asked what happened.
I told him everything, the teacher's
            part and mine.
He replied,
Saying it was his job
And that I had a point too.
He said again he'll just give me one.
I told him there was small justice,
For saying that I got two.

ANONYMOUS, 13
London

98

My teacher

My teacher's like a battle tank,
Roaring at the enemy
The enemy is us
And the roaring is the lessons.
He keeps us in a prison camp
Torturing us each day
And he will keep on torturing us
Till our minds are worn away.

RODERICK MACDONALD, 13
Annan

My teacher

Too much class work
Too much home work
Laugh at his jokes
Not at your own
I do not like him
He does not like me
We are both even
Except he has a belt
That is my teacher.

BILLY PROUDFOOT, 14
Annan

My teacher

The sad, grey, schoolmaster,
Struggles up the hill by way of a bicycle,
It is old,
Much in need of repair,
The same journey to the same school,
For thirty years,
He could have arrived in style
He could have made headmaster.

The schoolmaster is too old,
He has lost his nerve,
Now he can no longer confront thirty faces,
Looking for every failing and mistake,
Searching, critically,
His glassy, deep, faraway eyes.

Since his wife left him,
He has worn last year's suit,
With worn down elbows, trousers crumpled,
Shining with grease,
Last year's shirt,
Frayed collars and cuffs edged with dirt,
He wears no tie,
That has been spattered with grease from his fried meals,
The schoolmaster lives on these and bread with jam,
He has sunken low since his wife left him,
Every day he weeps behind his desk,
Every day since his wife went away.

MARY MCNALLY, 14
Benfleet

I found out today, we're going wrong

You don't know the hell I go through
When I'm in trouble
And everyone else is free
Waiting takes so long
When you're worried.

So sad to see you angry
So sad to see there's nothing there
'Talking to you is like talking to a brick wall.'
Nothing is achieved
Nothing is achieved.

All I want is to get out
There's nothing more you can do for me
There's nothing left
We're going nowhere.

But I'm not blaming you
I'm blaming the system.

CHLOË ALEXANDER, 15
Highgate, London

My teacher

Her old wrinkled face
Crushes my fears.
Her hair is grey,
Her eyes a misty blue.
We all fear her stingy stick
That hangs beside her desk.
She snarls as she speaks,
And her legs creak
Like rotting floor boards.
Her long nose
Pokes into my business
As she walks to and fro
Like an angry pigeon.
Her veins showing
Through her thundercloud stockings.
When will the frightening nightmare end?

JONATHAN TAQUI, 10
Ravenshead

My teacher

He mumbles on,
His good-natured eyes
Laughing at some ancient historical fact.
He walks round the room
Determinedly thinking of
What to say next.

His hand, deep set with veins
Searches in his pocket for his spectacles
He talks of Hereward the Wake
As he fumbles.
The lesson ends
And he disappears.

CLAIRE FIDDLING, 13
Falmouth

Jump boy, jump

Sandpit lay, its wide open space before me.
The crowd gathered around,
All eyes on me.
I stormed along the run,
Jumped.
Fat pig-faced man yells out
'Do it again,
JUMP BOY, JUMP!'
I ran again,
Failed.
'JUMP BOY, JUMP!'
I ran again
Fell flat on my face.
After that about fifty pigs laughed.
It's incredible,
That man said he believes in God
Yet he did that to me,
Destroyed my dignity.
Nobody lets me forget it
That morning,
And I don't forget either,
The pigs,
And the biggest pig
Chiding
'JUMP BOY, JUMP!'

KEVIN HEWICK, 14
Leicester

My teacher

My teacher has big eye brows,
Big as two foxes tails.
His eyes are like saucers,
And his nose as long as a woodpecker's beak,
His legs are like tall trees,
His arms like two long tables.
And all he shouts is,
'Get on with your work.'

JULIE BOTWOOD, 9
Llanwrtyd Wells

I sit here in my bedroom
That is strewn with books
Which come and go and blur
Before my eyes.

I will learn and look
And wish and wait
Like my million other compatriots
And with them, at the bell,
Pour it out on uncompromising paper
For an uncompromising examiner
Who has never heard of me,
To pull to pieces and say 'yes' or 'no'
'Pass' or 'fail'.

He holds my life in his flitting pen
But he couldn't care, even if he knows it.
He just wants to get through
As many lives as possible
So he can go home and sleep.

KAY FRANCES HARRISON, 14
Roston

The supermarket

I managed to squeeze through the door
And greet the hot, bustling crowd which awaited me.
It's as though I were squeezed into a small sardine tin.
I reached for a tin of peas
And found the whole lot rushing at my feet—
The pressure, the heat, the tension.
I moved on, trying not to crash against the wall.
Everyone seems in a hurry
As though the world were to end in five minutes.
I finally managed to get my few bits and pieces together
And now the wait,
The wait that really depresses,
That really tenses my nerves.
I stand lonely, uneasy—
The line moves,
I relax my muscles and fight to keep my place
As a fat lady snatches at a packet of Cadbury's Smash,
And another lady lashes out furiously at a small child
Who pesters her for an ice-lolly.
Once again the lines moves
And I move too.
A wasp stings an assistant—
This holds up the line even more.
I wait, now annoyed and still depressed,
I wait for ten minutes.
The assistant finally comes back,
Her arm clumsily bandaged.
I await my turn ...
At last it comes.
I put my bits on the counter—
She tried to reckon up my things,
She reached for a bottle of orange squash
But knocked it on the floor

Causing an even longer delay.
At last my chance came
To greet the fresh air once again.
I rush to the door,
A refreshing breeze greets me —
Everything so different
So calm, so free.

RAMONA HARRIS, 11
Stepney, London

Beach pollution in the year 2001

We're going to the beach today
My dad will drive us there
We're going to play in the mud and oil
And watch our portable colour T.V. set.

We'll paddle in the oil pools
And sit in the slime
And among all the litter
Who knows we might even find something of interest.

DIANNE ROBINSON-TODD, 11
Southport

The underground

Taking the escalator, I lowered myself down, down under
the ground to the awaiting monster.
A large crowd was waiting impatiently.
A small child walked to the edge of the platform and
was on the verge of falling, when her mother
let out a shriek and grabbed her,
And an old man sat in the corner sucking a pipe, half
asleep.
One lady was kicking and thumping a cigarette machine
to find the drawer was stuck.
Dirt, sweet wrappers and paper covering the floor and
overflowing out of garbage bins.
Outside an office a foreign porter was glancing at his
watch to find the train was ten minutes late.
As a sound is heard in the distance, people sitting down
gather their luggage as a gentle breeze warns them
of the train's arrival.
People bustle to get on and off the train.
It pulls off, leaving the unfortunate ones behind for
another boring wait
As the action repeats itself.
On the circular walls there are advertisements for films.
Another mechanical monster has pulled up for more
subjects,
And as I walk into this everlasting tube I have a sudden
fear as the doors close behind me.
I am on my own.
I want to get off but now I am imprisoned in a cell that
has been locked and the key has been lost.
As the train chuggs off I look to see the walls zooming
past the windows.
The green and red eyes show the way.
I just sit and wait.

SHARON HARRISON, 11
Stepney, London

Poem about trains

On warm nights I would hear them,
come secretly from nowhere
to illustrate my dreams
and trying to pass unnoticed
so that nobody knew
but the owl and I.
The owl was startled by their suddenness.
I was only moved to wonder each time
where these strange rumblings came from,
where they went to and why
where they went and why.

' ... and being confined to metal rails they remained at all
times firmly within man's control while he in turn was ruled
by their limitations. Theirs was great strength but, above
all, disciplined strength.
    Then came the motor-car ... '

And when the trains had gone,
as fast as they had come,
to some foreign place, I would wander
to where it was still again, where I
could almost hear the silence, smell the
trains and feel the stars in the gentle grass.
Why did they come so humbly, so finally,
as though ashamed of their
simple perfection?

I fancy now that I sometimes can hear them
on the edge of sleep;
But I am still an adolescent dreamer
remembering the trains
as my father remembered the horses,
and wondering who will remember
the motor-car.

SIMON NORTH, 16
Winchcombe

My future

A midnight jet
can hardly be identified,
on dark and unknown expeditions of the sky,
as more than a passing engine—
an unseen mechanism, progressing
through heights unrealized inside late houses.

But I looked up last night
and read in the quiet sky
the exact passage of the pilots
and fifty hidden people
seated and ascending the evidence of a journey.

Distance had accepted the loud machine
so secretly.
It had vanished, but its diagonal presence continued
    unalterably,
a faint geometry, placed in the sky with dissolving ends.
Unsupported,
tilting in gradual ascent above my window.

In the pale midnight, unable to sleep,
I watched until its whole white length
had been received back into the night sky.

ANNE HOWESON, 18
Nr Westerham

112

The concrete chimneys of fumes and fire,
Why, this is not what my heart desired.

Where are the people so kind and sweet?
Where is the countryside I so longed to meet?

I breathe the fumes of smog and dust,
The flats and sky scrapers I shall never trust,
I sit and watch the planes go by,
My future, oh GOD!
I could almost cry.

BARRY WILLIAMS, 12
Nr Wrexham

Timeless,
Godless,
Savages that lurk in the deepest universe
Shapeless paradise their home,
Gases they breathe
Cyanide they eat

INTIAZ MALEK, 14
Stepney, London

My future

Why are you crying, Mother?
My future stretches before me like a sea,
Your past is dead and gone like a grave,
And yet I am the lucky one
Aren't I, Mother?

Why are you crying, Mother?
A mechanical brain and a plastic heart
will make sure I do not die,
P.V.C. steaks and Vitamin A
will make sure I do not starve,
Coronation Street and football pools
will make sure I do not think,
Won't they, Mother?

So why should you cry, Mother?
There is carbon monoxide for me to breathe,
And D.D.T. for me to eat,
There are concrete blocks for me to — occupy,
So why?

FIONA MORGAN, 15
Gerrards Cross

114

They are coming for my mind today
because I dared to
think.
And in this world of machines
no-one thinks —
not even them.

But I was not born with a mind
just to feed on pills
and press buttons all day long.
I was born to think
and live
and to be free from such
monotony.
So I thought:
of life without machines
and tablets for meals,
of time of my own
and meaningless words of long ago
like happiness,
love,
and peace.

But while I was thinking
I forgot to press that vital button.
Then they knew —
So they are coming for my mind today
and I shall never think
Again.

JANE CROOKS, 16
Mansfield

A long pathway
my future stretches before me
cluttered with grey concrete blocks
that soar up into
the rolling sky
and clip the smooth spheres of the Sun.
The many windows
fixed everywhere will
reflect my image
when I pass by,
and the glass curtain
that now covers my path
will disappear slowly
as my life goes on.

SUSAN BONES, 12
Dovercourt

Obituary on the demolition of a house in Grove Lane, Camberwell

On the first day
I saw a woman
Dressed in a jumble sale
Eating a meal at four o'clock
She sat on the steps
And I felt sorry for her
And the house.

On the second day
There were no windows
And in place of a roof
A dull, grey sky:
The men had come
To demolish.

On the third day
It was a hollow shell,
The wall-paper brown-stained
Torn and peeling
Could be seen by all
— But no-one stopped to look.

On the fourth day
There was smoke in the air
Dust round us
The stone crashed around us
And there were men with dirty faces
And it went.

Today
It was a hole
I stopped to see
The sand and rotten wood:
The broken bricks
And solemn cavity
That was once a house.
But no-one seemed concerned.

MARIA DAWSON, 15
Dulwich, London

Rain runner (on running to a car in the rain)

Escape we must!
By flare of lamplight—
Flickering silver,
Wet and lethal,
Hard and cruel—
Colours in the asphalt beckoning.

Run, though,
Clatter, splatter
The hurried feet go:
New freedom from the first, long closure
We must now know.

Pin points of blemishing rain,
Dart-like, wing-tipped, finger thunder-bolts.
They flash and part;
And soon we are there.
The cold, wet handle.
The press.
That automobile smell.
And in.
Rain runner, you are home!

ROBERT SEATTER, 15
Surbiton

The accident

It was almost seven o'clock
A youth on his motorbike was having some fun
He was going full speed at a lady pedestrian
When he neared her
He swerved clear
To the path of an on-coming lorry.

He cleared the lorry
Only to crash into a car
The lorry hitting the car
The car turned over
The youth in his last seconds
Thought of his motorbike.

Two weeks old
Now its only good for scrap
Then he thought of himself
Nineteen years old
Now he is only good for scrap.

JIMMY MANSON, 15
Kilmarnock

My kitten

On Friday 9.30 a.m.
I heard a kitten cry
I went looking for it.
It was in a tree across a river
I wondered how it got there.
So I swam across
but it was no good
the current was drawing me away
I wish I was in a boat
Then I was shouting for help
no one heard me
I was just going over and then I fainted
when I woke up the dock attendant said
'I saved your life'
so I thanked him and said,
'I have to be on my way
I am going to save a kitten.'
'Where is it?
What colour is it?'
'It is black,' I said.
'You nearly died for that kitten.'
Then he said,
'It was my kitten it always goes up there'
So then he sat down and cried.
I said
'Don't cry.'

KELVIN SAMUEL, 15
Spitalfields, London

120

What can it be
This curious anxiety
It is as if
I wanted to fly away

But how hard it would be
I have never flown in my life
And I do not know
What flying means

I have all I need
Seed and water and air and light
Why then do I weep
And heave my head and wings
Against these sharp wires

while the children
smile at each other
saying
'Hark! how he sings!'

MARTHA CHARALAMBOUS, 15
Holloway, London

Lonely albatross,
Soaring above the deep,
Against a noonday sky
Of azure blue,
In which the white hot sun hangs
Like a mirror in a blue silk curtain,
Though reflecting nothing,
Revealing no secrets.

Lonely albatross,
Hangs among the fleecy clouds,
Silver wings embracing the unending sky.

Lonely albatross,
Catches the passing day,
With an unflinching stare.
A rim of pink appears in the west,
And the sun sinks like an apricot
below the horizon,
Filigreeing the sea with golden threads.
The sky flushes peach,
And night descends upon the world,
Sequinned with stars.

Lonely albatross,
Follows the path of the shrouded moon,
Across the purple ocean.

JANE RICHARDS, 12
Whitton

Revenge

Gliding swiftly with the wind,
Roaming, never stopping going on and on,
He stops occasionally for a drink and then,
He's up away into the sky.
I wonder where he goes at night,
Hiding from all human beings,
His eyes shining in the dark?

His freedom, like the trees,
His food he catches himself
And he knows what sort he likes
For his taste is never wrong,
Scratching it with his paws,
Savaging it,
Blood-stained claws roam the world.

PAMELA BARNSTABLE, 12
Daventry

Minnow me

Weather changes like moods above
with smiling rainbows in the water,
rippled colour-bright but somehow
shallow, and cloudy clutter-skirt lace
of the summer-deep sky's airy daughter
pruning lily-pad and pollen-powdered face.

I do not ponder long the heavens,
where strut reedy harp and treely gods,
the Other World I can only reach by
larch on looking line, and swim instead
through water weedly ways of froggy pools
and over stone-down snuggled on the bed.

Care not what my future be,
I move with only present liquid focus,
I see not more than instinct's spectrum,
I do not search for other bigger things
for these can end, with ease, my silly fuss
and prove the joke sly Ambition brings.

TERRY EDGE, 18
Upminster

An old man with an eagle's mind

Often, coming through the clouds of the valley
I have seen him
And often, sitting by a tree
Under the moist morning sun.

I have often walked through many
A well-worn path
Seen many a building harsh
And cried a desperate lonely tear

I have seen the sun rise
Over morning's mountains
Snowcrisp colden wonder white
Seen the sun dazzling in full rich golden light

And I have seen a great lake
Between great mountains gently lap
And birds grab fishes in a buffeting wind
Out of a stormy ocean

But now when all thoughts return to one
I cannot stand as an oaken tree
And with my hands build dust into the lifefire
Of the sun
As a tiger in a manger
A man with eyes of sheer human power.

ANTONY BROPHY, 18
Twyford, Berkshire

Raven

Raven,
black by scraping roofs of night aloft
by
raping gentle clouds from far lost
forests
where dwell all the mad populace
of maniacs'
dreams.
Raven with your eyes of diamonds hoarded,
insane as morals
mad as cats asleep that twitch
at secrets worlds away
from us.

Raven
   claws that clutching
   beak that kissing
   just as lovers touching—
who knows who's missing
   someone's
serious-eyed lover tonight
when dreams break blood in bloodless rite
a jealous heart's dark flights
of fancy—
   flies in fancy, raven
   flies in
   contradiction of the
   sun.
Raven,
black as the black in a
blind blackman's eye,
   Raven
quick as the pump of a frightened heart,
Raven sure as the flow
of an artery's power,

Raven
o so little darkness,
who'd be lost in thunder cloud,

126

Raven
but such cunning likeness
with the host of midnight's crowd.

HAZEL SCHOLLAR, 17
Upminster

Disappearance

I saw a pigeon
flying across the sky
it was black and white
it seemed like an aircraft flying high
it flew up and down, round and round
saw some other birds it did
I think it was scared
it flew like an eagle
flew right to the sun
then it disappeared in the clouds

MARION SHEEN, 12
Stepney, London

Triumph

The world hears Wall Street wailing
It's slipping down the charts
That sound like snapping concrete
Is tycoons' breaking hearts.

Is that infection spreading
Will Hunger Marchers tread
Past pale and silent children
Who wait in line for bread?

So open up the window
In the highest building
Let the rotten system
Tremble on the ledge.
If it don't want to jump
We'll just have to push it
Right on over the edge.

ANNA CHINQUE, 14
Hackney, London

Young, gifted — but black

When Mebula Ramsandra
  was five years old;
His mother told him, that if he wanted
  to be a big strong man —
He'd have to drink all his milk —
  and he did.

When Mebula Ramsandra
  was seven years old;
His teacher told him
  that if he wanted
To go to a grammar school
He'd have to try harder with his homework —
  and so he did.

When Mebula Ramsandra
  was fifteen years old
His lecturer told him
That if he wanted to be a lab technician
He would have to go to University —
  and he did.

So ten years later
When Mebula Ramsandra
  was twenty-five years old,
A big, strong, clever, educated postgraduate —
The man on the other end of the telephone said,
  if he wanted to work for him,
He'd have to be big, strong, clever, postgraduate —
  and white.

VALERIE NOBLE, 15
Shoreditch, London

Stephen McCarthy's death (the system)

Arrested with violence, that's the law
Battered and bleeding on a Police cell floor
Begging for help at Death's door
But that's the system, nothing more.

Happy house, full of children,
Laughter, shouting, never quiet.
Not much money, but love for everyone
And happiness that shines like the Sun.

Suddenly! a cold hard cell.
Empty! No comfort, just pain.
Eyes full of hatred, that stare now and again,
Then loneliness, darkness and more pain.

Time stands still, but the hurt goes on.
Blackness everywhere, peace at last.
Don't wake up. What for?
You're better off dead, that's what they want.

Questions asked, but nobody answers—
Nobody dares, what does it matter?
Who cares?
Stephen was nineteen, but now he's dead.

DAVINA PARKINSON, 13
Islington, London

Judge!

Straight, stern and grand
branding people jailbirds for life.
Square face, steel eyes, thin
mouth and pointed nose,
sharp as a pin.
Long white wig over the shoulders.
Red robe with glistening medals.
Oh thou merciful Judge.

CHARLES FETHNEY, 12
Willesden, London

Police

Police are good and sometimes bad
Police are very kind.
They walk along the streets at night
To see what they can find.

ANONYMOUS, 12
London

The judge said 'sit down boy!'
and dry up your tears
you're going to borstal
for two or three years

So kiss me goodbye mum
and say that you're mine
I'm going to borstal
for two or three years

There's bars on the windows
and bars on the doors
there's bars on the ceiling
and bars on the floor

You'll knacker yourself

FRANK and TERRY, 14
Camden Town, London

The joke is on you

You had yourself a good time,
And you had yourself a scene,
But over the sound of
     rock 'n' roll
Did you hear a scream?

Well, when they shot
     George Jackson
Did you shed any tears?
Or moan in frustration
When Jake got fifteen years?

When the wine ran
     free
And you had to be
Amongst the cool crowd,
Did you hear the dying
As they moaned aloud?

It's over now,
Forget it,
And don't take heed of me.
I'm just angry
About life's reality.

ITHAMAR BANCROFT, 18
London

Cast a saffron shadow

(to the memory of George Jackson)

Cast a saffron shadow
Over a shiny sea;

Light a lamp at evening
And let it shine for me;

Plant paper flowers in forests
There to let them grow;

Then trap a mind in prison
But it still is free to go.

LYNNE HUGHES, 18
St Albans

Black power
Yes, Black power
The owners of the world
Black the creators of the world
Black the white
White the black
The creators
Black the humans.

I.M., 14
Hackney, London

'Britain expects...'

The man who points the finger, has
   for centuries been asking each one of
   us to rally round for 'the cause'. We are
   not expected to question his authority as
   we all seem contented in our evil ways.

When asking yourself the ludicrous question
   'Who is he pointing at?' tell yourself that
   He is being very rude in pointing, and
   You staunchly refuse to take any notice
   of a man without Good old British Manners.

If the question of guilt arises in your puny,
   unquestioning brain, tell that rude, pointing
   man to sod off! Tell him that times have
   changed and you don't want to be a part
   of the system which has to kill to survive.

Tell him, in no uncertain terms, that you
   and only You, can judge what is
   right and wrong for yourself and that you
   feel quite cosy in your semi-detached
   hovel which is a front for your rebellion.

I remember once, I saw a man pointing
   at me in the street. Bloody cheek! I went
   up to him and chopped his silly arm off
   for being so damned rude and persecuting.
   Why should I fight for Britain, I'm black!

REGINALD GAMBIER, 16
Bromley

The dream of the mad man

The man is white with fear
He's running very fast
The eyes are wet with tears
Thinking of the horror that has happened in the past.

At night he cannot sleep
He has to look out of the window
To have a little peep
To see what's down below.

The lights of fury
Burn like hell
He's thinking of the jury
Who sent him to the cell

The windows barred
The doors are tight
They will not open
Though he tries with all his might.

ALAN BOYLES, 14
Durham

The few

Here they are
the feeble few
that have dared deride
mankind's trust

But are we
the feeble few?
Do we pass tests through?
Are we just?

Here am I
I want to have
a small amount of time
to break the crust

In a line
degraded are they
A small amount of time
I want to trust.

Prison clothes
what price to pay
a judgment on their crime
can we be judge?

have we the right
to keep them here
have we the right
to set them free?

GILLIAN P., 14
Durham

No rough boats (headlines)

Eyes in a bath of silence,
The tides of light washes soft upon them—
  A whisper in its wake;
  If you put your ear to mine
You'll hear the salt's sad sandthem.

Yet sounds pound foundless in us now
We've no profitery forge to cast their sense,
What meanings now are made on ripples
—We make littleword messages,
Put them in fragile tight-necked bottles,
  Then set them precariously afloat,
  And trust to kindly wind
  And goodly waves and
  No rough boats to break them.

TERRY EDGE, 18
Upminster

138

You

You are to me a Sunday morning
smelling of fried bacon and promises of more.
You are to me the honking of city cars
that spell gypsies and tambourines.
You are to me a majestic sultan
being fanned by ostrich feathers.
You are to me a white sports car at 95 mph
       that nobody else has.
You are to me life, my friend.
But what am I to you
a child?

GILLIAN P., 14
Durham

My hero

Clothed in black he rides through the night,
He bids me a farewell and gallops away,
The horses' shoes I can hear fading in the distance,
Everything is quiet and I feel sad,
Shall I ever see him again?
I turn away to my cottage which now looks like a sad white
    dog,
And the honeysuckle like drooping chains,
I think of the darkness,
And of my hero.

ANNE MARIE HANCOCK, 11
Ermington

Snails

Snails are hermaphrodite
(Which doesn't mean they hunt at night
Or that baby snails are excessively fat
No, it doesn't mean anything like that)
It means something like this;
    First they kiss
        Then they mate
            Then they separate
                Then they BOTH reproduce
To some people this idea may be new
But I can vouch it's perfectly true
If only God had had the foresight
To make us all hermaphrodite!

DOMINIC HODGKIN, 12
Spitalfields, London

140

Dear heart

When you see me standing there
And you feel as if your heart pounds out for me,
Don't force it back in again;
Pluck it out,
And with cupped hands bring it to me
That I might hold it in my own
To warm and shelter and keep alive.
And when I have loved it all I can,
I shall, oh so gently, replace it in your burrow,
So you may bleed it warm for me to love again tomorrow.

DINAH JEFFREY, 15
Highgate, London

My hero

The dark like a funeral march bearing candles creeps away.
And in the moment, brief, that hangs suspended is
Infinity, before the dawn.
I dream of my Hero.
Removing me from worldly care: severing
My chains.
We are free to fly: Brushing clouds with
our wings, grazing past the sun.
Only he could make me so
Free.
From lies, from greed, from hatred.
Anonymous
Radiating love to bind the universe.
Then the moment snaps, and as the sun
Melts by morning lethargy,
I am alone.
Yet he is there, a feeling deep
Inside me.
We can change the world
Tomorrow.

JANE THOMAS, 15
Rugeley

And you are the one
Who has freed me from me
Made me run free
Forget all the knots and varnish
Cool veneer
I put on to please them at home
Counting minutes
Watching neighbours
Sleeping Suburban slumbers
I'm not middle class in the sense they are
My values are wrong
A joke for a laugh is
The only way out of the truth
They can find
And you are the one
Who means more than they

TERESA NOWELL, 15
Barnet

On a visit to apologize

We sit, I below you as you wish;
In pale yellow room where cold, harsh sunlight strains the
     air,
Threading transparent strands
So we can see ourselves, too clearly.
Like a child in chilly waiting room,
I anticipate movement,
Using my conceited self-warming thoughts to protect my
     heart, and muffle my face.
See, as lemon as your yellow hair, that flows over neat
     shoulders,
Without visible ensnared tangle —
The liquid light surrounds you.
Move those mechanical eyes, glaring displeasure.
With well timed, piercing stares of sarcastic meaning.
Raise those fair eyebrows in contempt;
How exactly that tongue touches your teeth.
In quick darting motion,
Adding indifference, and friendly wit,
To enforce the argument of the eyes. Grey as stone.
The whole face, tilted back and up, glares down;
not in anger; but in bitter, faked, mocking;
Knowledge of self-right, gives force to your superiority,
As the pointed nail, brushes your cheek about the cold
     smile
That clothes mistrust, disappointment, and bitter pain.
I'd rather you flew at me and tore my aching eyes out —
For love betrayed,
Than sat in curst controlled unapproachable scorn,
Leaving defenceless,
Your repenting fawn.

SYLVIA GIBSON, 17
Chingford

144

We sat
My boyfriend and I by a pond.
We watched the sun glimmer and dart on tiny ripples.
The two trees by the bank I imagined,
Were in love like us but they looked so old.
One was choked by ivy the other bent and crippled.
A bramble bush on the bank an ace of many thorns.

It was hot
The cross around my neck chafed me so I took it off
And held it in my hand but it slipped through my
Fingers and fell into the shining water.
It was quite deep there and the water very clear.
Off came a shirt, my boyfriend jumped in and
Came up dripping wet but dangling my cross
From a finger, I was pleased.
My lover,
My hero.

JENNIFER MILLER, 14
Great Abington

The fall

Diaphanous grey mist he felt, and saw purple jagged peaks
Etched into a milky sky, a saw's edge hanging pale—
Cream, turning cobalt; as a distant, tarnished silver
Disc slid upwards and changed to flaring gold.
Water poured from the rock bowl's
Lip, and he stood holding dominion over
Fish, glistening in the pool below.
Climbing, reflected warmth of sheer rock at his back,
Fly-like, he held hard, as the multiple eye
Trapped the swooping freedom of the hawk
Diving in the shining morning
       —for ever—
         in the memory of his camera.

Dazzling rock-face forced him away with shrivelling
Heat, and the cool spray of the white cataract's plunge gave
Shaded rest. Fleeing the glaring sun across the sandy
Rib, she found him, and beneath the dusty pines
They fused aeons of the sun's glory to theirs,
Blending all time in the foundry blaze of their
Moulded, twining forms.

Rain dripped from the tall pines—primeval masts rising
    from
a Sargasso of putrefying brown undergrowth. The
Maggot crawled from the core, amongst the sodden cones
Sunk beneath their feet. Weight and volume increasing,
    water,
Smashing to the mossy boulders from above, made the pool
Deep, covering the rib of sand, until it was too dark
To offer relief from a dying sun.
Climbing, icy trickles in the moss replaced the river's
Writhing mists, and crumbling rock made feet
Slide; slither of movements with slipping feet, and the
Joint of a rib was broken in the man.
So they returned to their separate homes.

Spewing garbage bins gaped at sheets floating in smog,
    making her
Friendless: overtime left him weary: they avoided first

Neighbours then parents, now creditors: here only
Cataracts of chlorine mix grease in a chipped sink,
Eyes reflecting hire-purchase bills: a struggle in dark, silent
Depths, with the approach of cold staring stark—
A nestling also dies, when the grey cold
Labyrinths of sensation grow numb.

PETE BERNARD, 17
Hornchurch

The dreamer

From the house he travelled,
Through time,
Cutting the distant thread
Into the new world
A shiny star
Where he would be
Adam,
And the star the Eve.

INTIAZ MALEK, 14
Stepney, London

Today could have been a good day,
But as I sit in bed and look back,
I know it wasn't.
For today he left me,
And I'm not sure how I feel,
Another boy kissed me,
And I smiled.
Today he said it's finished.
And looked very sad.
We were both cut up.
But we came out smiling,
And laughing at the way we were.
Maybe that's how it should be.
The other boy asked where he was.
I said he'd left me.
He said he didn't know about love,
Kissed me
And I smiled.

MARY WATTS, 14
Chesterfield

Wedding day in Milward Street

A tide of lamentation has arrived
And swept upon the shore of Milward Street;
Moshe Berger is getting married,
A devout jew: a Yeshiva* boy
So there are hebrew songs
And random singing
For a marriage must mean celebration.

The grey prison slate bricks
Support the crippled houses of Milward Street
Already a Jamaican family, the Ranahoops
Have left behind empty rooms
With invitations,
For dossers to sleep away reality.

Somehow, the sun begins to shine
For a wedding day in Milward Street,
As practised voices and familiar faces
Climb into a waiting car
And slowly pull away,
Leaving a smoky trail behind.

ANDREW STROWMAN, 18
Bow, London

* Yeshiva is a Jewish institution where boys study to become wise
men—Talmud Chochom.

She

She had golden hair
She had blue eyes
She had a pale complexion.
She had all these.
I admired her
I even loved her
But
There was somebody else who
        admired her
Like I.
Someone got close to her
There was a car crash
And that was that.
I went to see her in bed
It was horrid,
Her face was cut
Her hair was stained with blood.
I still love her ...
            ... but she died
            and there was no-one else.

ROBERT NEWTON, 14
Swindon

150

Rain

Rain and you
Are soft as petals:
Wet
And dreamy.

Rain looks,
Rain sparkles,
Rain cares little for life.

You
And I
Share an individual fruit pie
In love
With each other
And the rain.

ANDREW STROWMAN, 18
Bow, London

Weeley Blues (or the awful truth about Sheelagh Macaulay)

Sitting alone in the company of many,
There's an emptiness inside me.
There's a feeling now inside me
That something there is gone.
Surrounded by kind people,
I am lost.

Although I only knew you
For a short two days,
I know that for that time
You were a part of me.
I feel that now I truly know you well.

Even if in the future
I will wonder what I saw in you,
As I write these words—I know.
How can you walk out of my life like that?
How can you leave me so?
How?

BRIAN ROBINSON, 16
Forest Hill, London

I sat in the library
Amidst a world of knowledge,
And listened to the traffic, distantly outside.

Footsteps, hard upon the wooden floor,
Echoed down the passageway.
Her footsteps perhaps,
Walking away.

I stared at the white, clean ceiling.
My hands felt the smooth skin
Of an old, leather-bound book.

And after that:
The next day came,
As most days do,
After the day before.

BRIAN GOODCHILD, 17
Buckfastleigh

Hiroshima labour pains

This agony is the truth,
The truth of what happened so long ago,
When you were young.
How was it now?
Ah, yes—
Between each sigh of pain you feel the
            thrust of the past,
Between each howl you hear a deeper moan,
Between each throb of your belly you remember
            the throb of his flesh,
And,
As you relax a while,
You recall a similar relaxation,
A similar silence,
As the semen of wrath flowed into your soul.
And now that the placental silence is over,
And the dreamy embryo has turned,
And the agony is at *your* door,
How is it now?
Now that the pickle-blue child writhes in *your* arms,
Now that he sucks at *your* breast—
Now that the blood eases itself from *your* burns
And the fears from your eyes?

OMAR EBRAHIM, 15
Coventry

154

To Anne Frank

all that remains
a brown-edged memory
forever smiling.

And I remember now, all those deeds that made me
weep,
scuttling mishapes blur the eyes,
all the eyes—looking; smarting, through intensity
stand to see only soot-black windows
and cities burning beneath the frothy sky.

And then, you, had disappeared also
and had left me alone, to weep
for the Hungarian children, waiting in the rain,
waiting for hours—to be gassed
and you had cried and said:
   'Look, look their eyes ... '
And you cannot imagine how soon, most of us came
to the end of our tears ...

DAVID LEWIS, 16
Scarborough

My hero

My atomic club
My nuclear sub
—normal bastard son
I fallout
To make love
With a gun
Every child that's born
Tends to the slaughter
In the Avenues.

Supplementary Space
Acrid face
I abort birth in the blue-green
Open seas
A rough tarpaulin veil
Tempestuous hail
In the wheel-house squall
Of my mind
And my stale Atomic eyes fall
Out of my face as it rips
And my teeth become like chips
And as my knees become like mud
My groin as water washes them away
I call
'Give me my atomic club
I'll show them the sun
Of a thousand million deaths.'

ANTONY BROPHY, 18
Twyford, Berkshire

I saw him lying there
Yellow as a lemon
They said I had to kiss him
For the last time
So I did
He was there no more
The shovels helped to
Cover him
He was there no more

PANAYOTIS ZENIOU, 17
Islington, London

Vietnam

Bleached scar on the face
Of civilization
How many years now?
But how many more?
How many lives now?
How many to come or to go?
Another lover sits and weeps
More soldiers end.
And the day and the dark are the same
Where war can descend.

LYNNE HUGHES, 18
St Albans

Letter home from one of the boys out East

(Will the real Captain Amerika please stand up!!)

Ward 5,
Saigon Military Hospital
28.10.71

Dear John Wayne,
      I've seen the film before.
         best wishes
            B. Rogers

BRIAN ROBINSON, 16
Forest Hill, London

Waiting

The sky above my head is grey, and cloudy
As my mind, for
I can barely tell
If it's night or if it's day, just
Waiting,
Debating in my tired out mind.
Will I live, will I die?
Where are my fellow men?
I don't hear their voices any more
And my heart is sore
As my hands are raw, and cut,
But,
Still I cling to my rifle, and,
Still I am surrounded by mud
Black as an eerie bog,
Staring at blood and clinging fog.
My thoughts fall into a wilderness,
But for the
Knowing,
The growing
Of fear
And the waiting.

NIKOLA GREENFIELD, 15
Shaftesbury

160

A war
Ruining innocent people
Like me
I sleep in a dark ditch

Bombs and deadly gases blowing
Causing Death and Destruction
Everywhere

A rat moves slowly
Towards my foot
My first reaction
To stamp on it

The rat struggles
It stops
It is dead
I myself have created death

I pick it up
Should I eat it?
Can I?

I throw it away
Disgusted with myself
I huddle and wait
I wait for the next move.

JENNIFER MORGAN, 14
Archway, London

Londonderry air

An incubus in embryo
Waiting for to sprout and grow
Into gross repulsive gore
Blooming into civil war.

LYNNE HUGHES, 18
St Albans

Ulster

Thirteen died, what for?
For hate or for war?
They're in their coffins at last,
People filing past,
Sobbing, weeping, crying,
They think everybody is lying —
But they're not.
Little babies crying in their cots —
The ones who done it think they're brave,
But they're not,
They ought to be enslaved.

TONY HUSSEY, 14
Spitalfields, London

My future

Belfast is my home town.
Belfast is a fighting town.
Will the fighting ever end to make all
our homes safe and sound?
Will the clothes be better or worse?
Will I pass my exams? I wonder.
What sort of job shall I get?
Who shall I marry? how many children
Shall I have one, two, three, four, five or
more?
Will they be boys?
Will they be girls?
Or will they be both?
Will I be alive when the world
ends or will I be dead?
Belfast is my home town.
And I wish it would become a
peaceful town.
To let people live in peace.

MONICA DAVEY, 10
Belfast

163

The army

The lone soldier
Watching and waiting
Gun in hand
Watching and waiting
Listening looking
Peering touching
All five senses
Watching and waiting

The khaki soldiers
Looking for trouble
Pretending that others
Are looking for trouble
Looking, making
Wanting, finding
But the people all know
The cause of the trouble

The lone soldier
The khaki soldiers
All young men in their prime
Sent to Ireland by the bosses
To die before their time

But do they know why
They are doomed to die?

ANNA CHINQUE, 14
Hackney, London

Dean

My small son died yesterday.
In a virgin room so white and clean.
And, 'Christ! I want my son!'
'Dean! Oh! Dean'
Twelve hours ago a bullet from a Protestant,
Or was it a Catholic?
Or merciless hell was it an I.R.A.?
He was playing marbles yesterday,
His hair shone in waves, and those sparkling eyes,
Sometimes, you know,
He'd run into my arms.
And we would fight on the grass, and I was happy,
Because I could say 'My son is a fine son.'
He was a good boy,
He'd laugh at my jokes, even when they weren't funny.
And I would sometimes kiss Dean's cheek.
Seeing his limp body decorating the gutter,
His eyes bulging,
And a small trickle of red blood drip from the hole
In his head.
I hate Catholic!
Venom for Protestant!
And no place in my heart for God
The Irish murderers stopped for a second and listened,
When I told them that Dean was no religion
Because Dean had never been christened.

PETER GRESTY, 17
Chadderton

Soldier Brown

John Brown was happy and content with life:
He had a child who was to him the earth
And all its gladness; and he had a wife
And company of friends who loved him well;
He had a healthy home in which to dwell
And steady work. So distant seemed the birth
Of trouble, and of times which were not free
From hardship and the need for charity.

But unemployment struck, and with the curse
of queuing and pursuing charity
Came discontentment in John's heart. Far worse
It seemed to him to queue and beg for food
Than starve; for though it toiled with humble blood
His heart was high and lacked humility.
And so to feed his wife and child, his plan
Was to enlist — A military man.

He learned the art of fighting, and he found
To be the target for a sniper's sights
Was made his task, and to ignore the sound
Of rebel rabbles clamouring to dig
His early grave. Condemned a fascist pig
By those who loudly called upon the Rights
of Man to work for all; they shot him down
And spat upon the corpse of Soldier Brown.

The demonstrators had enough to eat
And grew their hair to show that liberty.
They all agreed that people should defeat
The fascist pigs who try to tread them down,
And justified the death of Soldier Brown.
They all agreed *they'd* rather starve than be
A kill-for-money soldier; that the law
Wastes money; that no student should be poor.

The demonstrators all went home to tea;
They took their sugar with a liberal hand
And chose their cakes. For none of them could see

Young Widow Brown sit single in the gloom
By which her cheerless memory-haunted room
Was filled; and in her eyes she felt the sand,
By sobs of grief across the water thrown,
They'd shovelled on the corpse of Soldier Brown.

WILLIAM ROCHESTER, 17
Chatham

Jimmy and Janice (A night in Belfast)

O
Some warm circles of the fire
include us snugly in their
comradeship against the night —
sulkily hanging on the window ledges
and coolly-eyed gazing
through the shivering trees
as if to say I don't need your
silly short-lived heat, I've got
the flaming moon to keep me
safe —
but there's longing at
the tiny trembling of the door —
knob and there's faint little
firefly hopes a-shudder on the
glass,
   so you find some shady little corner
of your heart respond a little
like a
quiet uncertain grandad
answering to a word that
pulls him wake,
so even though the context's lost and the
meaning hard to grasp —
   to let some something lost
come in, to maybe shake itself dry,
unwrap it's shadowed form and
stand revealed and grinning with
delight in the horror of your solemn
recognition; then
make a nuisance of himself with
blabbing in your lover's ear and
filling out your bed and
never going out
   or to
go outside yourself and maybe
never finding who
the longing is
and always after longing for

some other shadows on your
lover's face to change her shape
to comfort your sweet
nemesis of youth—
    he'll speak out anyway
and maybe some will laugh a little
some will surely
pause, so please
O
Please dear god, spare me these spare
phantoms in my flesh,
leave them at my door,
then if it's asking not much
give my love the strength to
pinch or tickle
me awake just when I
would sleep
and maybe never want to wake no more.

TERRY EDGE, 18
Upminster

My future

My future,
A worry to everyone but me.
What will happen when you've left school?
Every night I get that question,
So I'm fed up of My Future,
Before it comes.

ALAN SCOTT, 15
Annan

My future

Once upon a clear day
My future, with the veiled and misted sun
Arose before me, on a pale uncertain horizon
Bathed in a shimmering haze of crystal lights.
Stray dream vapours curled and stroked the sky
And wove a lattice rainbow in my hair,
A snowdrop vision of love and innocence,
But as I reached out it slipped back over the lid.
Once upon a grey day
My future, with the bleak and grizzly dawn
Rained down before me in a blinding fog
And gurgled down the ever open drain,
A black hole gaping through industrial smog,
A dense machinery maze of grimy shafts,
Monotonous tooth-edged blades and grating dirt,
A looming ghoul of eternal pain;
Once upon a day.

VALERIE LEYFIELD, 16
Upton-by-Chester

My future

My future lies before me,
A whirlpool of degrees,
Of interviews, of competition,
That's what my mind's eye sees,
You can't back out,
And when you fail,
There's sorrow and disgrace
So you have to start again,
In this desperate rat race

Why can't I stop and think it
out?
Why is there such alarm,
When someone leaves this machine-like
world,
To live in peace and calm?
And when you're dead that's it!
Some young man fills the space,
And just a hunk of stone and
flowers,
Stands above your place.

JOHN REDSTONE, 13
South Norwood

172

I think I'll be an executive.
That's what I think I'll be.
My Dad says I'll be on the bins.
That's what he thinks of me.

ALAN TWIGG, 12
Widnes

When they ask me
what I'm going to be when I leave school,
  I say I'm going to drop out,
  and go to demos to scream and shout,
You should see their faces fall.

They say be like us
take no notice what's going on around,
  I say no man! I'm going away,
  to shout loud and clear what I've got to say,
But they'll never hear a sound.

They say you know it'll never work
Can't you youngsters understand?
  We're only going to stop the wars,
  we'll all go mad and change the laws,
One day we'll get this land.

They say have a fag love,
Go on mix in, you'll only live a lie,
  We're up the pub, it's a Sunday,
  Down the dole on a Monday,
Just how can I reply?

KAREN JAQUES, 15
Enfield

Me fairthers a coalman an' carries coal,
Mutthers a 'ousewife but she doh care
An' Me, I'm a nothin' I just grin an' bare.

Butcher, bairker, fireman, cop,
Theers enuff jobs 'ere t' stock a shop,
Me fairther said, 'Now cum on lad an'
Be a coalman like y' dad.'

Me Ol' fairthers still 'eavin' coal,
Me Mutthers still workin' t' th' bone,
I might decide t' be a tutor,
But theers plenty o' time t' decide my future.

MARK BIRCH, 13
Walsall

Only hate, greed and desire

Whilst
walking through Everyone
or was it
Everyone's nightmare?
I spied a poem
lying there.
My eyes
saw only Hate, Greed and Desire
amongst its burning plea.
I Spat at it
and
Stamped it out.
It Splintered
into a million broken letters.

Then,
Everyone awoke
and
    saw only shattered glass
where once a Mirror had been.

MARTEN CLIBBENS, 15
Wantage

176

A letter of application

Dear Sir,
(de dah, de dah).
I am seeking employment,
(de dah).
I admire your organization
(do I hell)
And I hope that you can offer me
A post.
I write shorthand at one-twenty
And type at fifty—words per minute.
I keep books,
Have (reasonable) looks,
Can supply reference
A dozen certificates
And the fixed charming smile
Of a robot.

At the end of it all,
What shall I get?
A little brown packet
With which to console
A lost identity—
A breaking heart.

ANITA HARBOTTLE, 18
Bristol

My future

My future is coming
But what a one!
Keighley is losing all its fun
All the mills are shutting down
in Bradford and Keighley,
Leeds and Ilkley.
What a loss!
I do not know what my future will be.

We have buses and trains
Cars and planes
But not for the people of Keighley.
Perhaps I'll be rich
And have more than a stitch
My own car and a plane
Still, poor old Keighley down in the drain
I do not know what my future will be.

ANTHONY CROSSLEY, 14
Keighley

The world – and my future

As I come over the hills the lights of Shaw dazzle me!
Yet in the day I see chimneys black and grimy.
The dark of night covers up the black polluted air,
In the dreamland of night, the light seems like a fire
Waving in an eternal pattern, like a cobra, to Oldham.
In the night the whole scene is glorified,
But when the day comes – instead of beauty –
Belching, whirling, and belching yet again, smoke fills the
    air.
The distance is still the same ...
But instead of trees and flowers – factories and smoke!
Yet once it was pure country till industry, science and
    brick
Darkened the face of the earth.
I think to myself 'God, what sort of future is awaiting
    me?'

JEREMY BISHOP, 10
Nr Oldham

From a hill

Looking down on the lights of Sheffield
A hundred thousand jewelled fires
Burning on a black velvet ocean,
If I look into someone's eyes
Maybe the lights will be reflected
Christ, who's got eyes as wide as the world?

JOHN RICHARDSON, 16
Colchester

My future

I would like to be an Astronaut
And land on the twinkling stars
And wait for the counter down to say nought
Then off I go to Mars.

Up into orbit changing course,
Watching the instruments alter
Speeding on for millions of miles
We must never falter.

Speed a million miles per second
Mars coming into sight
Be there in two hours ten minutes
At the moment there it's night.

Landing retros firing now
Open the chute to land
Now we're hitting the atmosphere
The view from here is grand.

Going out for a walk on Mars
Oxygen is O.K.
There is a crater made of chalk
I'm going there right away.

Now get ready for blast off from Mars
Everything going well
Goodbye Mars, beautiful stars
My visit to you was swell.

Hitting earth's atmosphere again
Heat shield white hot
Splash down in the clear blue sea
What a very careful shot.

Divers open the hatch now
'Hallo Bert, Hallo
Now you're a Hero, come on out
The dinghy's waiting below.'

TIMOTHY JACKSON, 9
Reading

Atomic Age

Now there is silent eternity
Godless race wandering across the black universe
Extinguished
Extinguished from the intelligent flame of life.
The dark burnt shapeless globe
Remains fatherless
Sunless.

INTIAZ MALEK, 14
Stepney, London

Inbetween sketches

Inbetween sketches
> the artist sighed

Inbetween dances
> the ballerina cried

Inbetween papers
> the businessman lied

Inbetween wars
> somebody tried

CHLOË ALEXANDER, 15
Highgate, London

My future

I will live, before I die
In the jungle
In the trees and on the plain
I will fight, although in pain
Though I'm hurt, though I cry
I will fight and I will die
For freedom.

And I will not be alone
In the jungle
For men are there, and men will come
And they will fight
And they will die
But surely they will overcome
For freedom.

PHILIP JOHNSTON, 17
Rainham, Kent

At night the foxes howl,
At night the dogs bark.
The light of cars
Flash over the landing.

At night on the church
I hear the owl hoot.
Then I hear Mr Man
Come home from work.

Then all the lights go out,
And it goes very quiet,
But I still hear the foxes
And hear the dogs bark.

And still I'm here.

CLAIRE FITT, 9
Birmingham

List of Poems

187